Chiang Mai
Bangkok
Koh Chang
Koh Samui
Krabi
Phuket

By: Erik & Julia Wirdheim
Illustrations: Prema Jatukanyaprateep

Vera and Victor discover Thailand

Mini-Morris

Morris

To our parents,
Åke & Saale Hanson, and Eva & Lars-Gunnar Wirdheim,
for early contributions to our love for travelling.

Vera and Victor like going on holiday. This year they're going to Thailand. Although it's the middle of winter, they are packing summer clothes, because in Thailand the weather is hot all year round.

It's a long flight to Thailand. Victor has packed a computer game and Vera is taking her sticker book so that they've got something to do on the journey.

What things do you take when you go on holiday?

"Can I pack Morris?" Vera asks. "You're not allowed to take real dogs to Thailand", says Mummy.

Morris has to stay with Granny. Luckily, Mini-Morris can come along. Vera never leaves home without Mini-Morris!

Do you have a special friend that you never leave home without?

They've arrived at the airport and it's very busy! There's a lot of queuing to do! A lady wants to see their tickets and passports. And there's a machine that looks inside their bags to check what they're bringing on board. Some things are not allowed.

Mummy can't take her nail scissors; they're too sharp. "Good", thinks Vera. "Then I don't have to have my nails cut."

The airplane is huge. You have to sit down with your seatbelt on. But Vera needs to go to the toilet! "Wait", says the air hostess, "you can't go just yet. The plane is about to take off!"

Once they're in the air it's time to eat! Their food comes on a small tray, with little knives and forks. Later, Mummy and Daddy watch a movie. Victor plays with his computer game, but he falls asleep and drops it on the floor! Do you think Victor will remember his game when they get off the plane?

Vera hugs Mini-Morris. "I wonder if they have dogs in Thailand?"

They've landed! The air hostess finds Victor's game on the floor. Isn't he lucky!

They've travelled a very long way. Victor has shown Vera where Thailand is on the map. It's on the other side of the world. Although they've just woken up and had breakfast, it's already late in the day. "When it's daytime at home it's night-time in Thailand", Mummy explains. "It's called time difference."

Time to queue again! They have to queue to get off the plane and queue to show their passports. Then they'll be able to get their bags.

You can easily tell the people who have come off the same plane. A lot of them have blonde hair like Mummy. But the Thai people look different. Their eyes are more narrow, and they all have black hair.

A bus takes them to the hotel. There's traffic everywhere! The bus drives on a bridge high up in the air. There are lots of roads underneath. This busy city is called Bangkok and it's the capital of Thailand. "Look how many cars and buildings there are!" says Victor. "That's because so many people live here", says Mummy. Vera spots a dog all alone on the pavement. "What's he doing there all by himself?" wonders Vera.

At the entrance of the hotel, a lady bows to them holding her hands together. This is a Thai greeting and it's called a "wai". They do this in Thailand instead of shaking hands.

Outside the hotel they see a little house on a stand. It's called a Spirit house. Vera thinks it looks like a doll's house. "Don't touch the house", says Mummy. "It might upset the Thai people."

They believe that it's a lucky house and that if you leave food and drink underneath, it will protect the hotel.

It's very hot and Victor wants to go swimming. Luckily the hotel has a swimming pool! But where is it? How can Victor ask if he doesn't speak Thai? The Thai language is quite difficult to learn. Look how different the letters are!

Mummy tries asking in English. But the lady just smiles. Thai people smile a lot. Usually it means they're happy. But sometimes it can mean "sorry" or "I don't understand".

Finally, there's the swimming pool!

No dogs allowed! Hopefully no one will see Mini-Morris hiding in the bag...

Today they want to explore Bangkok. Outside it's very hot and sticky, so they decide to take a boat trip. The boat is long and narrow. It's called a longtail boat.

They cross the big Chao Phraya river. There they can see big, slow boats carrying cargo and fast express boats that stop at different piers. They're almost like buses! "I wish we could take a boat to school everyday!" says Victor.

The boat takes them down some small canals. It's much quieter here. Many years ago, Bangkok had lots of canals. The postman used to deliver letters by boat and people took boats to go shopping.

They see some children swimming by a small pier. "Oh", says Mummy, "the water looks very dirty." Suddenly someone grabs their boat. It's a lady in a funny straw hat. She smiles but she has no teeth! Her boat is filled with souvenirs. Daddy buys Vera and Victor t-shirts. It says THAILAND on them.

Do you have any souvenirs at home?

The tour on the boat ends at a park with snakes and crocodiles. Victor is excited, but he and Vera like dogs more than crocodiles. What about you?

Now everyone is hungry and tired. Luckily Thailand is full of places to eat! Some are directly on the street. The street stalls are noisy and smoky and smelly. Next to the stall there are tables and small plastic stools for people to sit on.

Mummy and Daddy, Vera and Victor decide to go to a place that's more like a restaurant at home. In Thailand people eat with a spoon and fork and everyone shares the food on the table. "But what can we eat?" wonders Victor.

Daddy orders lots of different dishes. "We will have to try and find out what we like", he says. Vera and Victor decide they like rice and noodles. Some dishes are so spicy that Daddy gets tears in his eyes. Thai people love spicy food and put chili on everything.

What would you like to try?

Thai food

Vera and Victor like fried rice...

...and fried noodles

...but the fish still has its head on!

The curry is hot...

...and the soup too

...but the spring rolls are mild!

For dessert you can have mango with sticky rice!

You can also order Western food

... if you don't like Thai food.

Although it was really tasty they couldn't eat it all. "If only Morris could be here now! Do dogs like spicy food?" Vera wonders.

On the way back to the hotel, they pass a fruit seller. He has two big baskets filled with fruit, hanging on a bamboo pole. He takes his shop wherever he goes. Have you ever seen a walking shop before?

Vera and Victor have never seen so many strange fruits. One is small and quite hairy. Another is white inside with black spots. One fruit looks like a hedgehog! It's called durian and it's so smelly you can only eat it outside! But some fruits Vera and Victor recognize from the supermarket back home.

Which ones have you seen before?

"Yuck!", says Victor. He has spotted another little stall selling strange things. Fried insects and little octopus. "Can you really eat THAT?" he asks. "Yes", Mummy explains. "Some Thais eat these as a snack instead of crisps." But Victor prefers crisps. "No way would I eat that!" he says.

Could you eat fried insects?

The next day the family goes to see some temples. Temples are Thai people's churches. They pray to a man called Buddha and not to God. The temple is painted in beautiful colours and is very glittery. Outside there are statues of big snakes, monkeys and giants. They guard the temple against evil spirits.

In Thailand they think feet are dirty, even when they've just been washed! So before going into the temple you must take off your shoes. And if you have to sit down, make sure you don't point your feet at the Buddha. It's difficult to sit like this, Daddy thinks. His legs hurt.

Outside the temple a woman is begging. Daddy gives her some money. There is a small dog by her feet. Vera thinks he looks hungry. "Maybe he can have some food now", she says. Thai money is called baht. For a poor person, a few baht can be a lot of money.

From the temple they take a tuk tuk. A tuk tuk is a cross-between a motorbike and a car. It has no doors or windows. The whole family squeezes in. "Hold on tight now!" says Mummy before they speed off.

The traffic is very bad. They decide to get out and take the sky train instead. Taking the train can be faster in Bangkok because there are so many cars. Sometimes the traffic doesn't move at all. The sky train goes high up in the air, on a bridge across the city. Victor likes trains!

On their last day in Bangkok, Mummy, Daddy, Vera and Victor all go to the big market. Thai people like shopping and the market is very crowded. Vera holds on to Mummy's hand tightly!

Mummy sees some beautiful silk to buy but she thinks it's too expensive. She smiles and offers a lower price. The stall holder says "OK". "In Thai markets you can bargain like this", Mummy explains. Thai people always smile and are friendly, so it's important to do the same and not to get upset. "This was a good price", says Mummy when she has finished bargaining. Many things are cheaper in Thailand.

Have you ever been to a market?

The children are hot and thirsty. In Thailand you need to drink a lot. But not tap water! You buy bottled water. Victor buys a fizzy drink, which he gets in a plastic bag. The children drink it with a straw. You should try it sometime!

Then Vera needs to go to the toilet. But look at it! It's not like the one at the hotel!

They walk past the pet section. Too late! Vera has seen the puppies and runs towards them. Daddy knows that some of the dogs can be sick. He says firmly: "No, don't touch!"

"Come and ride on my shoulders instead", says Daddy. She can now see over everyone's heads and points the way out.

Vera and Victor wake up early the next day. "Hooray, today we are going to the beach!" Victor shouts excitedly as he puts on his swimming trunks. "But why are you packing the suitcase?" he asks Mummy. "There are no beaches in Bangkok. We have to fly there", she answers. But it won't take long.

After a short flight they take a bus to the hotel, but it's not like a normal bus. They have to sit on long benches at the back. "What a funny bus!" thinks Victor. "Oh", says Mummy worriedly, "there are no seat-belts! Make sure you sit still, children!" Sometimes things aren't as safe as they are at home.

Along the road they can see coconut trees and banana trees. It's hot and humid in Thailand. We call it a tropical climate. The trees here like that.

When they arrive at the beach, Daddy is happy. "It's lovely to be so close to the sea!" he says. They're staying in a beach bungalow with a straw roof. Vera and Victor want to go in the sea straight away. They've been looking forward to this so much!

"Don't go swimming without us", Mummy says to Vera and Victor. Thai beaches don't have life guards. They all go down to the sea and the children jump into the water. "The water's so warm, it's like a bath!" Victor shouts.

There are lots of things to see and do on the beach. If you're lucky you might see little crabs. A dog has! "Poor doggie! He doesn't have anyone to take care of him", says Vera.

In Thailand the sun is very strong. Mummy keeps putting sun screen on the children. Daddy didn't put any on yesterday so he's really red now and has to sit in the shade. He couldn't sleep all night!

Have you ever been sunburnt?

Finally Mummy can relax. She has a massage. "Ouch", she yells when the lady kneads her too hard. Daddy's not relaxed! People keep trying to sell him things all the time. On the beach you can buy fruit, drinks and clothes - even paintings!

There are lots of children to play with. Victor goes snorkeling with a friend. They wear masks so they can look under water. They see colourful fish and coral. Vera is building a sand castle with a boy who speaks another language. Where could he be from?

The next day the family goes to an elephant park. The elephants show them what they can do with their trunks. They can carry big logs and even paint pictures with a paintbrush!

Vera and Victor go for a ride on an elephant. He's huge! They have to use stairs to climb onto the elephant's back. The elephant keeper sits between the elephant's ears. It's really bumpy when he walks!

Would you like to go for a ride on an elephant?

After the ride, Vera and Victor feed the elephants. It tickles when they take the bananas with their trunks. "Oh, he ate the peel and everything!" Vera giggles.

Elephants are large and very friendly animals. "I wonder what other animals there are in Thailand? Are any of them dangerous?" says Victor.
Let's find out...

There are mosquitoes in Thailand. Don't forget your mosquito spray!

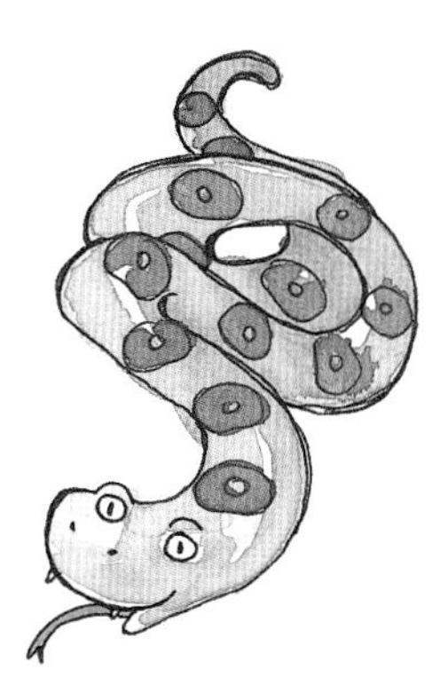

You can find snakes in high grass.

You might see a monkey on the roof!

You might see a cockroach on the floor.

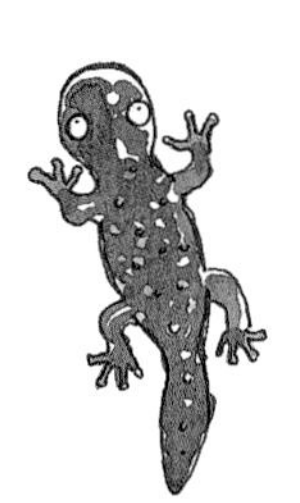

Geckos can stick anywhere - even on the ceiling!

The sea-urchin lives on the bottom of the sea. Watch out - it's spiky!

Don't worry - there aren't many sharks.

The jelly-fish's tentacles can sometimes sting.

The next morning Mummy wakes them up very early. "Do I have to go to school?" Victor mumbles sleepily. "No, but I want to show you something", smiles Mummy.

Out on the street they see monks walking in a row. They are wearing orange clothes and have shaved heads. Every morning people in the village give them food. Monks cannot own anything. They must only think about Buddha.

At the end of the row there are boys just a bit older than Victor. Thai boys are often monks for a while. They go to school and learn about Buddha. They help to clean the temple and do things to help others. The boy monks can't bring toys from home. "At least they have lots of friends to play with", says Victor.

When they have gathered their food, the monks go back to the temple. After their meals there is often some food left over. The monks give some to the poor, but they don't forget the dogs. The temple is filled with dogs! "The monks help people in need, so they must take care of the dogs too!" Victor explains to Vera. "I'm glad someone looks after them", thinks Vera.

"But how's Morris getting on at Granny's?" Vera says. Suddenly she really misses him. "What if he doesn't recognize us!" she sobs. "We'll see him soon", Victor comforts her, "we're going home tomorrow!"

After a long trip, Vera and Victor are home again. They can feel that they have been to the other side of the world. Victor can't wait to go back to school to tell his friends all about it. Vera is really happy to see Morris, and he is really happy to see them! He does recognize them even though they're suntanned. I'm sure they smell just the same. What do you think?

Wirdheim Culture AB

Writers: Erik and Julia Wirdheim
Illustrator: Prema Jatukanyaprateep
Editors: Lois Abbott, Joanna Slaney
Layout: Kanchalika Kampananonda
Printed in Thailand 2007. 6th printing.

ISBN 91-975099-1-4

www.VeraandVictor.com
www.WirdheimCulture.com
info@WirdheimCulture.com

Thanks to: Lucy Castle, Kristina Hansson, Paola Hjelt, Magnus Larsson, Ulrika Larsson, Sofi and Daniel Miari, Åsa Spolander, Britt-Marie Sjögren, Hanna Wirdheim, Boel Wästberg

For ideas and support without which, this book would not be possible